The Blue Suit

A 9/11 Memoir

By Michaela DiBernardo Ferrigine

never forget
Michaela

Published by Metal Dog Press, LLC.

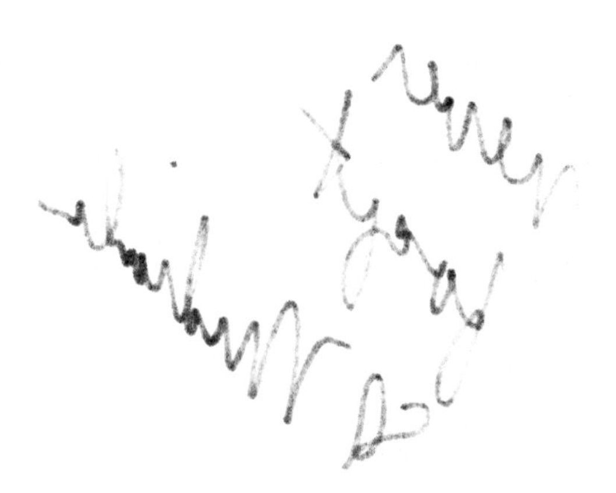

This story is dedicated to first responders and survivors everywhere—who carry the lives of those who perish within their own.

* * * * * * *

The PATH train rumbled slowly across the Passaic River outside Newark Penn Station, on toward the next stop, Harrison. Feeling lucky to have gotten a seat on the crowded car, she attempted a nonchalant glance down at her bright, blue suit, which should have been a perfect choice for today. But now, an hour into her commute, she had doubts.

Earlier this morning, in the predawn dark, she had parked her car at the Allenhurst train station and turned off the engine. Leaving the auxiliary on, she breathed out slowly, and prepared to listen to the radio until the early train pulled in. She wriggled further into the seat and smoothed the silk of the dress's skirt. This suit, she thought, (although more snug than she cared to admit) still fits pretty, darn good. She had smiled as she adjusted the radio.

"You can't tell yet," the radio DJ gushed, "but if you thought yesterday was some beautiful weather—well, today is going to be absolutely PERFECT!" Yesterday had been nice; her fifth day back to work. It was a perfect beach day, for those lucky enough to have the day off.

"So, let's start the day with U2's hit single—wow—almost a year old: *Beautiful Day* offa *"All You Can't Leave Behind."* She leaned back, and breathed in the thumping of the opening chords and salt air drifting from the ocean.

Drinking in the music to the sound of quiet dark, she sat this way—letting her thoughts wander to this evening, already anticipating a return home. As the last reverb faded away, she turned the ignition key towards herself and squinted into the dark, waiting for the familiar glow of dawn from somewhere below the horizon.

Reaching into her leather bag, she withdrew a photo of two small toddlers, beaming as they held a tiny newborn. Her heart caught for a moment; then she moved quickly to return the photo to her bag. Something stopped her, and she changed her mind, tucking the inhabitants of the photo safely into the sun visor.

She sighed once with reluctance. The end-of-summer breeze off the ocean mingled with the smell of her children on her jacket, and kept her in the seat. Smoothing the lovely fabric across her lap, she looked again for the sky to lighten.

But the dawn was not ready to appear, so she allowed the distant sounds of the train whistle to call her on to the next place.

The PATH train jerked once, returning her thoughts to the present. Another jolt—then again—and, squeezed somewhat as she was into the dress, she couldn't properly recover her seating. The suit began to rebel.

It had begun to creep up thighs that had not been this ample at the time she purchased it, and the constant seizing and jerking of the train necessitated that she tug—first the left, then the right—on both sides of the hem. Frowning self-consciously, she performed an awkward, tick-tock shifting in the seat for longer than she would have liked.

When the Barami store had opened in the underground mall at the World Trade Center, she had been thrilled. Her work had her continually on and off planes. The ability to purchase a new suit, or blouse, for a business trip during the daily commute was invaluable. Working mothers filled the underground mall daily, sometimes shopping for school or the holidays, still retaining the ability to make a train. This particular suit had been purchased nearly a year ago, when even the smallest size they carried had to be tailored to fit her slim figure.

But now—after returning from maternity leave—she needed to leave the very top of the dress zipper open a bit in the back, hidden under the jacket. Frowning again at her thighs, she straightened her back in the seat, attempting to lessen the pressure her post-baby body was exerting on the delicate silk.

The PATH train doors slid open at Journal Square Station. A crush of men, many appearing to be of Middle Eastern or Indian descent, crowded aboard. They were all dressed neatly—similarly—in dark slacks and checkered shirts, buttoned to the throat. She listened as they began discussing whatever their days' events would be, some softly, while some spoke loudly and gestured in an animated fashion.

Averting her gaze, she tried to decipher their speech, with its odd cadences and song-like quality. After listening for several minutes, she realized there was not one word that she could recognize, or translate. She allowed her thoughts to wander elsewhere, to work, clients.

Turning slightly, she noticed a beautiful, young dark-skinned woman, her hair pulled neatly into a bun at the nape of her neck. One thin, delicate hand clutched the hanging metal strap overhead tightly, while the other arm periodically flew into the air like a bird, to check her balance. The tiny woman turned toward her, revealing a pregnant figure.

"Oh!" she exclaimed at the sight of the pregnant girl. "Oh!" she said again, and jumped up, motioning for the woman to sit.

Before the woman could release the strap above her head, a man moved to slide into the vacant seat. Placing a leg in front of him to block the maneuver, she reserved the seat for the intended. The woman nodded in thanks and settled into the seat with a heavy sigh.

Now, she reached up for a strap. She felt the suit jacket restrict her upper arms, which were thicker than in the past. The jacket tightened across her back. The train jerked again, and the commuters swayed together. Turning to hold onto the overhead bar instead, she felt the material of the dress make a vulgar grab across her rear-end. Accepting this state for the moment, she stared at her reflection in the windows, created by the blackness of the tunnel outside. For a moment, she did not recognize herself.

The train slowed and squealed, lighting the tunnel outside with sparks. The train rumbled forward, and the darkness gave way to the artificial light of the underground station. She looked at her watch. It read 7:35. The lighted display above the door read: WTC.

The conductor's voice announced: "World Trade Center, last stop. Last stop, WORLD TRADE."

The doors slid open, and the commuters shuffled slowly up the long stairways, on to the escalators, heading into the subterranean mall above.

She walked quickly to the escalator, which continually turned its patrons onto the smooth floor that passed before the retail stores: The Gap, Godiva, Strawberry, and others. People poured into the mall from other trains, other subways; from the Hoboken PATH and the Cortland Street station. Some people shopped before work. Some hurried on to get another train. And some continued upstairs to their offices in the Twin Towers, high above the streets of Manhattan.

And still many others filled the vestibule—where the indigent had claimed refuge, their sheets of cardboard leaning in urine-stained corners. One tall door was held open—every day—by the same smiling, homeless man.

Today he proudly held the door, allowing the warm breeze to welcome the commuters as they moved on to their work, their everyday lives, spilling out of the doorways of the World Trade Center, into the dazzling September sunlight.

* * * * * * *

She sat somewhat uncomfortably at the large, conference room table, happy to hide the dress skirt that crept up her legs. Shifting self-consciously, she yanked on first one side of the dress, then other, as her boss tapped the glass-topped table impatiently with a pen. "Well, it appears he has forgotten about this morning's meeting," he said finally, indignantly, "so I suppose we will have to start without him."

"I believe he did have a meeting in midtown this morning," she offered, "at Brahman, I think."

"Yes, and I believe it was a 7:00 am meeting, if I'm not mistaken." He looked at the stainless steel encircling his wrist and continued, annoyed, "And it is now nearly 8:45".

The office occupied space in the historic Trinity Building, and the double-hung windows—unbarred and old—were thrown open wide to let the beauty of the day into the stale conference room. A wall clock ticked loudly in the tense silence.

He turned on her now. "Weren't you supposed to be at a meeting today?" His brow furrowed, probably still thinking of the other employee. "I mean, shouldn't you be at a meeting this morning? Now?" The pen tapped impatiently on the glass. He continued, "Fiduciary Trust, right?"

She took a deep breath. "Yes. I was supposed to do a meeting at Fiduciary this morning. I left the file on your desk last night, with a note."

Last week, the woman who was the head of the trading desk called her. She was going to be out of the office the following week, on vacation. "You can come up and meet the rest of the desk on Tuesday morning if you want," the head of the desk joked, "but you'll have to do the dog and pony show when I get back." That was fine, she answered, and would come up Tuesday morning anyway—the formal meeting could wait until the head of the desk returned.

But her friend called yesterday. "Listen, the head of the desk won't be here this week," he said. "Don't feel like you still have to come up here tomorrow to do a meet-and-greet."

"No way!" she replied. "I'll just stop up to say 'Hi' to everyone."

"Listen," he had said kindly, "you just had a baby, and have the two little kids at home besides." His tone was quiet. "You don't have to come all the way up here, carrying boxes of Krispy Kreme, or omelets, or whatever you were planning to bring." He continued, "Save yourself the trouble; wait until the head of the desk gets back." She could hear the ease in his voice, "Don't worry, we'll do business—you've got the account."

She had smiled into the phone, "You are a good guy. Thank you."

"You are most welcome," he had said.

The boss continued to tap impatiently, as she relayed the information to him about the canceled Fiduciary meeting. He still appeared annoyed, probably not at her, but at the other sales person who was not there.

Still wanting to go over other scheduling for the upcoming month, the boss began again, angrily, about the errant employee, "You can't tell me he didn't . . ."

His sentence was cut short by the sound of a tremendous explosion. The heavy, glass top on the table slid into her midsection. The old building trembled.

“What the hell!” The boss gasped. “What the hell—what the hell was that?” His eyes were wide, his face was incredulous. “Was, was—that a bomb?”

“Maybe,” she said, oddly calm while extricating her body from between the chair and the glass, “maybe it was a gas main.” He jumped up, ran into the other offices and returned quickly.

He found her standing before the open, double-hung windows, staring skyward.
“Where . . .” her voice trailed off as she looked out of the window, “where is all the paper coming from?” she wondered aloud.

It appeared oddly reminiscent of a ticker-tape parade, except the sheets of paper were full, like from a propaganda bomb she had seen on television. They watched in silence as the multi-colored paper floated down, littering the Trinity Graveyard below.

One piece of paper, an office memo, landed delicately on the windowsill in front of her. She picked it up. The edges were charred and black. Leaning out from the open window, she watched as what appeared to be cotton candy pieces of insulation fell—faster than the rest, in spiraling descent—trailing smoke. They appeared to have some sort of plastic attached to them.

Standing before the open window, he remarked again, "What the . . . HELL?" He turned to her, blue eyes wide with purpose, and said, "We need to go downstairs—NOW—and see what's going on!" He shouted for the operations clerk to accompany them.

She touched his arm, and nodded silently to the wall of glass belonging to the office building diagonally across from theirs. He followed her gaze. "Look . . ." she said quietly, ". . . at the windows."

Across the expanse of the Trinity graveyard, the reflection in the glass windows showed a huge fire dancing—at the only building large enough to obscure the sky.

The Trade Center was on fire.

* * * * * * *

She walked out of the rear of the building onto Trinity Place to the sound of honking and shouts, and an odd flurry of office paper and small pieces of debris. Cars had backed up on Cedar Street and Trinity, and without knowing what was going on about them, drivers swore angrily at one another, honking. All the while, pedestrians shouted to tell them of the fire above their heads.

Some cars managed to snake through and continued on their way. She crossed the sidewalk that passed before the cobblestoned interior of Liberty Park Plaza, where Trinity became Church, in front of Brooks Brothers and looking skyward . . . stopped.

Her hand flew to her mouth in horror and disbelief at what she saw. An enormous hole had been torn just below the upper floors of the North Tower, and black smoke was bleeding upwards from it. She stood near the base of the building, in front of the same PATH and subway entrance through which she had traveled only a short while ago.

"What happened?!" she demanded of a woman, also holding her hand over her mouth, staring upwards. The woman shook her head, and shrugged, unable to speak, it seemed.

She looked skyward again, and felt ill.

"That's Cantor, up there," she said, to no one in particular, " and . . . and . . ." Her friends, together last weekend, taking turns cradling her new baby . . . they were getting married this week. . . she felt sick, might vomit.

The offices of Cantor Fitzgerald occupied the highest floors, above the damage. In 1993, her brother-in-law and friends had walked down over one hundred flights of dark, smoke-filled hallways, but now . . .

Her mind raced: friends, getting married this weekend, were up there . . .

But whose families, what firms . . . were at the site of that gaping, smoking hole?

Again, desperately, she shouted to no one in particular of the gathering crowd, “Does anyone know what HAPPENED?” The sounds of sirens had begun to blare in the distance.

A man behind her offered, “Some guy said—it was a plane, hit the building.” She stared at him, as if he were an idiot. She, and the others that had gathered, looked up again.

Thoughts from the past raced through her mind with this

information, made calculations. Many times she had stood on Top of the World or had a business breakfast at Windows on the World. Twin propeller planes would fly up and down the Hudson River, through the clouds, far below the upper floors. She remembered thinking on a foggy day, if one of those planes did collide, it would certainly bounce off the hulking structures.

She turned to the man, with annoyance, "A plane couldn't inflict that kind of damage to a building of that size." She continued angrily, "It would bounce off!"

He shrugged. "That's what a guy said," he repeated defensively.

"That couldn't happen from a plane," she stated flatly.

Then a woman spoke. "It WAS a plane", she said. Now, they all turned to listen. "A commercial jetliner." They all stared. "I swear!" She continued, "It musta, I don't know, lost control or sumthin'." They stared at her, unable to absorb what she was saying. “It was . . . a . . . ‘UGE plane!”

People looked from her, to the building, in complete silence.

“I saw it,” the woman said, finally.

She stared up, numbly thinking of the people, on that plane, on their way to somewhere nice, or the people, sitting at their desks, at work early, who were now dead. Her mind churned, unable to compute, how a commercial airliner could lose control, why? Why was it so close to the city . . . was it trying to land? . . . thinking, thinking . . . how would her friends, above the site of the damage, all the hundreds of people at work already, how . . . how to get out? Her throat tightened, and tears began to run down her face.

The man spoke again, “They’ll probably get a helicopter up to the top. They can land on the roof. They’ll get everyone out.”

Objects were falling from the building.

But the smoke—black, ugly, thick—there was so much smoke. The people inside must be desperate, the heat from such a huge fire intense . . . her thoughts ran together, desperate for them. Hurry, she prayed, silently, please God, hurry. The sirens were coming closer, blaring, arriving.

The first fire engine pulled up Church Street, and police were blocking traffic. "Alright, alright, here we go, the Bravest are HERE!" a man said. A small, lifeless cheer went up from the crowd that had gathered. Then some clapped, and the crowd cheered again, more loudly this time.

The first firemen to arrive—some still not dressed—pulled before the buildings, jumped off the engine, and looked up. Then quickly, wordlessly, they grabbed their gear. Their faces were set, fearless. Without hesitation, they began running toward the burning building.

Immediately, right behind the first, another fire engine arrived. Men—fathers and husbands and brothers and sons—hanging from the sides of the engine, jumped off, grabbed their equipment, and ran to the Tower.

Then another fire engine pulled up, and—looking as if they had picked up off-duty firemen on the way—the men quickly, silently pulled on their gear, and moved to the building.

And another fire engine pulled up, and the firemen jumped out.
And another fire engine pulled up, and the firemen jumped out.
And another fire engine pulled up, and the firemen jumped out.
And another fire engine pulled up, and the firemen jumped out.

Now the sound of sirens drowned out everything, but still fire engines came up Church, and from behind, and from the east.

And still more fire engines pulled into the street, and men scrambled with tanks and hoses. They shouted only instructions to each other, none of them hesitating for a second to fight a fire over 800 feet in the sky.

And it seemed the fire engines loaded with firemen kept coming.

She looked up. The firemen had a long way to go, carrying all their gear. The woman who said she had seen the plane crash, turned to her and said, “You’ll see, they’re gonna save all those people. They’re gonna have helicopters . . . and everything.”

She nodded at the woman silently.

* * * * * * *

Then, a sound came from both near and far away.

It was a loud, squealing, roaring sound—familiar—but so out of context that it seemed very, very wrong.

Out of nothingness, the roar came, louder, immediately closer. Panicked heads began to turn every which way. The deafening sound had no source, but it grew painfully louder still, until it was all around them, deafening. People covered their ears with their hands, long before they saw its source.

Then it appeared.

A commercial airliner—engines squealing as it flew at terrifying speed just above the streets of lower Manhattan, passed behind the South Tower. She watched, in horrified disbelief, as the plane banked at a steep angle, turned, and flew directly—deliberately—into the upper half of the South Tower of the World Trade Center.

* * * * * * *

She thought she had heard the explosion that swallowed the plane and the upper portion of the building. But perhaps, she had not; there was only total silence.

She stood, unable to move, rooted in the space between the vanished and the newborn reality. Her mind imagined an unfolding, crackling sound.

But the world was completely, oddly silent. A fireball, giant and of the most intense orange and black, began to swell from the wound in the Tower. She watched it grow in silence, then race down the side of the building toward her.

This strangely muted world confused her mind and left her in a trance. Staring up, she felt the heat of the fireball and saw a large object falling from the sky. A mob of people had begun running toward her in slow motion, away from the building, toward the open space of the park behind.

A woman ran past her, mouthing the word, "RUN!"

Then, she realized, in an instant: if she didn't run, she might die.

Debris from the explosion was raining down from hundreds of feet in the sky. For the first time in her life, she felt a singular fear. Acting on that simple, terrified instinct, she ran.

* * * * * * *

Waves of people sprinted past in all directions, and her peripheral vision caught objects falling from the sky. The interior of Liberty Park was covered completely in cobblestone, and people stumbled as they tried to get out of the open area, away from the falling debris, to the shelter of the scaffold that surrounded the corner building on Cedar.

A heavy object hit her left shoulder, and she fell facedown on the stone. She felt someone's shoe step off her right calf, then another person ran diagonally across her back, and her chin hit the cobble.

Before the thought occurred to her that she might be trampled to death, two strong hands, one on her right and a different set of hands on her left, picked her up. Without a word, two men, one in a white business shirt and tie, the other in a suit jacket, lifted her up and off her feet.

Without once breaking stride, they ran while carrying her, until her brain made her legs work beneath her. Her feet found purchase, and started running. The man to her left simply let go, and ran toward Broadway. The other man placed an arm around her waist, and propelled her toward the scaffolding surrounding the building, placing her against the wall. He nodded to her, then he turned, ran east down Cedar Street, and was gone.

She watched in horror from under the scaffold, as objects fell into the open space before her. Inching her way along the wall, still in partial silence, she made room for others as they sought shelter. When she finally got to the corner, she turned and ran the last couple steps to the alcove of her building. She squeezed her body into a corner of the Gothic entrance, breathing rapidly in shock. A man grabbed her and shouted repeatedly and wordlessly at her. Slowly, as if coming up from the depths, she made out what he was saying over and over, "Are you hurt? Are you hurt?" he shouted, and pointed to the blood on her shin.

She finally screamed at the man: "There were two planes!" she shouted, "Two planes!! It wasn't an accident!"

His face was blank, still holding her by the shoulders, "What? No, there was one plane!"

"I saw it! I saw it! There was another plane! They're coming to kill people!" she shouted back at him.

Inexplicably, he shook her once, threw her back into the stone wall, and ran off. She winced as her shoulder hit the rock.

Getting to her feet and turning to the lobby, she saw her boss inside. She ran in and hugged him. He had seen it, too. "We have to go upstairs, and get everyone out." he said, but his words were still muffled. Nodding, she motioned toward the stairs. "No!" he insisted, "Too slow! We're taking the elevator."

* * * * * * *

Once all had been convinced to get out of the building, their small group gathered under the scaffold, amid a cacophony of sirens and screaming. A Port Authority officer walked back and forth on Broadway, advising, “Find shelter! Stay inside! Don’t panic!”

An NYPD officer shouted, “Get outta here! Get uptown! If you’re not injured, leave! Get uptown as fast as you can!” Hiding under the scaffold—against the building at the top of the basement stairs leading to Suspenders—they stayed for too long. Some others from their Floor trading team ran up. “We’re not hanging around, screw that! We’re gonna head uptown.” One of them, a trader from Rye, offered her cash in the event the ferry to New Jersey was still running.

She shouted to a Port Authority police officer jogging down Broadway. “Can we still get to Jersey?”

He yelled back without stopping, “Subways all closed! Bridges all closed! Ports all closed! Walk across the bridge if you can!!” She blanched at idea of not being able to get home.

Her close friend, a Manhattanite, said, “Well, there’s your answer.” He looked around at the others, who murmured about many different plans. “What? Listen, we can’t lose our heads.” His was always the voice of reason. “So, we hoof it uptown—no big deal. You heard the man—let’s get going.”

Another executive of the firm said, “Did you hear the other guy? No. We should stay right here, out of harm’s way. You go out there, you’ll get hit by debris, and maybe there’s a bomb . . . who knows?”

She looked at them at all, her feet only wanting to run, ashamed that she couldn't control the panic within.

Then, with all the gravity she could muster she said, "I saw where that second plane hit. They are going to have to save all the people stuck in the buildings." She took a deep breath, and continued, "I'm no engineer, but from where it hit, it looks like . . ." The faces around her stared back, listening. But she wasn't sure what they were thinking. She began again. "I think the top of that Tower can . . . fall over, collapse, maybe—into the streets for blocks around and then . . . There won't be anyone to help." She took a deep breath. "We should all leave —now."

The man who had advised them to stay scoffed, "Come on, do you have any idea what those Towers are built to withstand?" The officer of the company continued with a bit of ridicule, "Now you're panicking. You do what they tell you to do in a situation like this, right?" He smiled for effect, "You stay put."

She looked at him incredulously. "Well, I'm telling you, that building looks . . . looks . . . " her mind grasped for words, ". . . unstable!" The men all looked at her and were silent. She continued, "Like the top is going to fall off—over, onto everyone!"

She spoke loudly now, and fast, "I'm going east as far as I can, then I'm going uptown. Then, I'm going over the GW—if they let me." The group was silent. She was in full flight mode. "I'm going home."

Her friend, the reasonable one, nodded. "Okay. Okay. You're right." He kept nodding. "We should all leave—because we can. The fire, police—all those people trapped—they have enough on their hands." He turned to her, kindly, "If you need to stop, or you can't make it to the bridge, you know where we live." He and another got ready to start off to home, uptown, toward the West Side Highway.

* * * * * * *

Almost forgotten, the firm's data entry clerk sat on a duffel bag on the steps, shaking her head, crying silently. The clerk was young, and pregnant with her first child. She offered the girl a hand to help her up. "You can't stay here, okay?" she told her. The young woman began wiping her eyes.

The other men encouraged her to go. The boss asked the clerk quietly, "Where do you need to go?"

The clerk answered, with a slight Spanish accent, "I can go to my mother's, in Washington Heights."

A colleague nodded, and motioned to her, "You have to take her out of here. Now. She'll be moving slow. Ok?"

She nodded slowly in response, as if she didn't understand the charge she had been given. Then, quickly, she turned to the clerk with urgency. Perhaps a little too brusquely she said, "Okay, let's go! I'll take you to your mother's." The pregnant girl looked unsure. So she tried again, smiling this time, and said, "I'm going that way, uptown." The clerk picked up the duffel bag she had been using as a seat, both women covered their heads, and they attempted a sprint across Broadway.

The clerk stopped—unable to run—and turned to look back. It would be easier for her to stay put, on the stairs. She reached out to hold the girl's hand. "We can't go back," she said quietly to her. They crossed in front of the park on Broadway, turned right, and started jogging into the sunshine on Liberty Street.

The clerk had begun to sob, "I'm sorry, I can't do it! I'm too big! The bag—it's too heavy . . ."

"What's too heavy?" she looked at the clerk, confused, then down at the duffel bag the young woman was struggling with. Her mind couldn't place it. "Wait a minute " she said, "where did that bag come from?" The girl looked despondent. "Why did you take that bag?" she demanded. The clerk was silent. "What's in there? Gym clothes?" The girl began crying again. Exasperated, she ordered her, "It doesn't matter what's in it. You have to leave it!" and waited for her to let go of the bag. The clerk did not. "We have to move!" Her voice was raised now, and angry.

"Aye, Dios mio, I'm so sorry!" The clerk sobbed, "I can't leave it."

"What? Why?" And without waiting for a response, she said, "Give it to me, then!" She grabbed the bag from the smaller woman, and her arm dropped. It felt like it was loaded with stones. "What the hell do you have in here!?" she demanded.

"It's my fiancé's, his textbooks . . . he just paid for them." She sobbed. "Aye, I'm sorry, I can't let you carry it. Please; it's too heavy!" The clerk held the strap and tried to take the bag back.

“GIMME the God damn bag!” she yelled and grabbed it from her.

She ducked her head under the strap and slung the bag across her chest like a mail carrier. It bit into her left shoulder, and she growled before switching it to the other side. Grabbing a handful of silk lapel on the jacket, she turned it several times to create padding for her neck.

“Oh, I can carry it soon.” the poor girl apologized softly.

“It’s okay.” She returned to calm. “We just need to get moving.” Barely a block down Liberty Street people began pouring out of buildings, choking the sidewalks. They were jogging at first, then walking, then shuffling, in a pack moving east toward Water Street. A woman with a baby stroller was stuck in the crowd, unable to move forward more than a couple of inches. The infant kicked his legs and cried. She turned to the mother,

“Take the baby out. Leave the stroller.” The woman looked at her blankly, as the crowd continued pressing forward. She turned and raised her voice to shout back at the mother, “Take the baby out! Carry him! Leave the stroller!” The woman looked at her and began unbuckling the baby.

The sirens never stopped now, and people had begun running again. She took the clerk’s hand and made ready to cross the street toward the east. A slim black man in a suit stood atop a trashcan. Two women and a man stood before him, their hands folded in prayer. The man in the suit was preaching in a loud, clear voice: “The Lord is my Shepherd, I shall NOT want . . .” The sea of people crossing the streets didn’t allow for cars to pass. She encouraged the little pregnant clerk to walk fast, pulling her along, while the duffel bag cut into her neck, and banged into the small of her back. The minister’s voice followed them as he continued, “though I walk through the valley of the shadow of DEATH, I will fear NO evil!” He made no motion to leave, and she watched him as if a vision. His voice rang out loud; it did not waiver, “For Thou art WITH ME; Thy Rod and Thy Staff they comfort me . . .” The voice followed them as they ran.

They ran up Water Street, and she allowed the clerk to slow down. The uninterrupted noise of sirens and blaring fire engine horns filled the air. They stopped, turning to look back. Others had stopped as well. The crowd saw them at the same time: small black forms sailing forth from the upper levels of the burning towers. The unblemished sky silhouetted them perfectly.

The clerk covered her face and began sobbing and praying loudly, “Oh, my God, my God! No, no, no! Those poor people, they’re jumping! No! My God!” With each person, a horrified exclamation went up from the small crowd.

She stood and watched. Her stomach turned and rose up in her chest. A lump closed her throat, and there was no air. Pounding blood filled her ears, her head . . . mothers, fathers, sons, and daughters . . . Her mind whispered to each of them: you are not alone, you are not alone . . .

A low, rumbling sound began to shake the ground. "What is that?" the clerk asked.

"I don't know . . ." but she was already moving, "Let's go." She imagined bombs detonating in buildings to the south. They had gained some distance, but still the streets below City Hall had begun to turn dark, and the ground was shaking—an earthquake? "Move," she ordered, "you're going to have to try to run." The poor girl nodded, and she shuffle-jogged to keep up. The rumbling continued, and the sky behind them began to turn dark.

A young white man with a goatee jumped onto a trash can to get a better view. He scanned the area to the south, then turned to the people on the sidewalk, eyes wide: "HOLY SHIT!" he yelled, "The building is GONE!" The people who had not stopped slowed their pace to look back. Impossibly, as if by some trick, the South Tower was simply no longer there. No one could have survived a total collapse—the office workers, the firemen, the EMT's . . . they were gone. The strange, darkening sky was moving, coming their way.

Alarm bells were ringing in her head. "We need to MOVE. NOW!" she ordered the poor clerk, then stopped. Perhaps for the first time that morning, she looked hard at the girl.

For her stage of pregnancy, the girl was enormous. Her face was swollen with exertion and sorrow. Great, heaving breaths came from her as she sat on the curb, and dried white saliva stuck to her lips, and in the corners of her mouth. People stared at her as they jogged by.

A man stopped and asked, “Is she okay?” A foul-smelling breeze started to overtake them.

“Can you get her a water?” she asked the man, and he turned to the bodega owner standing behind him, who was holding a water bottle in his hand. She thought she heard the bodega owner ask the man for money. An angry exchange ensued over the price of the water, but the man won, and passed the water to the girl.

The crier on the trashcan sounded again, “That shit’s coming this way, we gotta, GO!” He jumped down, and everyone began to hustle north.

“Come on, you don’t have to run” she said gently. “We’ll walk fast, that’s just as good.” she told her.

“Oh, I’m too slow, too tired,” she moaned, “I’m so big . . . I can't do it!" She covered her face, exhausted and in despair. "What are we going to do?" She looked up, wiping tears from her face. "You leave, I'll rest here," she sobbed, "you have the kids . . . a brand new baby!" The young woman began sobbing again.

Her voice was gentler when she replied. "Think about *your* baby," she said. She felt badly, pressing the exhausted girl, but there was no other way "We'll take it easy," she said, "no more talking, just moving." Anxiety was rising up inside her. She felt danger ringing all around them. They needed to keep going. "And no more crying—you'll get dehydrated. Okay?" The girl nodded and snuffled. The ground had begun to rumble again, and the stench on the breeze brought with it a fine, choking dust. The clerk nodded and they were off.

Water Street faded into Pearl, and as they ran, became St. James, which carried them to Chinatown. She allowed the girl to rest at

Canal, then continued north, making their way up the Bowery.

* * * * * * *

After they ran, they walked—for what seemed like days, not hours. The sun burned high and hot in the cloudless sky. She had long ago removed the blue suit jacket, tying it around her neck under the bag strap. She didn't remember removing her ripped and bloodied pantyhose, or where she had left them. They had accidentally started west near Union Square, but she caught them quickly, and skittered back to 3rd Ave.

She had become edgy, anxious to keep moving, and mapped in

her mind what landmark would be targeted next. They stopped to check payphones, all of which had no service. As they moved uptown, they came across one or two phones which appeared to be working, but the lines snaked down the street, and service was inconsistent. Paranoid and nervous, she tried to give landmarks a wide berth. Somewhere on 3rd—east of the place between the Empire State and Grand Central, but before the long, steep climb toward the 59th Street Bridge—they came upon a car. It was tricked-out, gangster style, and parked at the sidewalk. The doors hung wide open, and a small crowd gathered around it in silence.

What would have otherwise seemed a strange assortment of people—young gangster-looking types, business suits, and restaurant workers—instead appeared together as if by appointment. One of the owners of the car had a radio playing loudly, to which the crowd was listening silently, intently. She and the exhausted girl moved in close to hear.

The broadcast told of other planes, hijacked for use by suicide bombers; it told of the Pentagon being under attack, more dead. The possible use of terrorists carrying low-tech, radioactive bombs was discussed.

New York City was frozen; all access into and out of the city had been shut down. "Wait," she asked nervously, to no one in particular, "how close are we to the U.N?" A young black man, looked up from conversation, uncrossed one arm and silently pointed east. He then continued to consult quietly with a manicured woman in a suit, exchanging information. They spoke in hushed tones, stopping occasionally to confer with two busboys from a nearby diner.

Yellow cabs sped by, devoid of fares. She continued to try to hail one for her friend, in vain. One stopped for a fare ahead of her, and as it idled, several young white men approached the cab, yelling and swearing. One of the men threw a bottle at the windshield where a Middle-Eastern driver sat. Two more young men ran up to the car, yelling racial epitaphs and picked up rocks or whatever they could find to throw at the cab. The frightened driver quickly sped away.

Stopping by a pay phone with a long line, the clerk asked if anyone was able to get service. "In-and-out," a person in line replied as they waited.

"Come on," she said impatiently, "I'm not waiting on this line."

The clerk looked around, and spotted a person talking on a cell phone. Cell phones had become fashionable, and were now carried by those other than physicians and executives.

The clerk seized on the opportunity, "Excuse me, can we use your phone? We were . . . um, down by the Trade Center . . . it's a local . . ."

The kind individual with the phone interrupted her question, "Of course! The service is spotty, give me the number—I'll dial for you." The clerk gave her mother's phone number, and was handed the phone.

She listened quietly as the clerk, crying, told her mother in Spanish of the awful horror and sadness of the day. Her voice was choked and overcome with emotion. The clerk hung up, wiped her tears, and held out the phone to her. She hesitated—she had friends who lived in the city. She knew what her husband, her family would tell her—order her—to do. She waved the phone away. The clerk was confused, "Your husband; you should call him, he will be worried."

She thought of the fireball, the abject fear—of a silent promise made in an instant. "I will call him," she said without emotion, "when I am close to the bridge." Others had approached to use the cell phone: service was dead, gone now. They continued north.

The buses that passed were packed, people inside squashed against the windows. Occasionally, one would make a move to stop, but there was no place where the tiny pregnant woman could get on.

At 93rd Street, a bus pulled over, and three people squeezed out of the partially open door. Running to hold it, she yelled in to the bus driver, barely visible behind a mass of bodies, “Wait, wait! Getting on, getting on!” The other passengers, held captive by their sheer number, just watched.

“No more room!” the driver shouted from somewhere behind the people.

“This woman is pregnant—she’s walked all the way from downtown!” She shouted into the partially open door, “please!”

The bus driver, a woman, shouted back at her “Lady, can’t ya see—we got no room!"

It was true; people were smashed up against the interior of the windows, and the open bus doors showed only a tangle of bodies.

"She can't walk anymore . . . please," she continued to beg, "she needs a ride." The driver didn't look sympathetic, but finally waved the pregnant woman on board.

"Where will you go?" her friend turned and asked her.

She answered without hesitating, "I'm going home." Her friend looked skeptical. "I'm almost at the GW . . . sort of," she added, with less certainty.

She stooped and gave the clerk a hug; she could feel everything that had happened that terrible day, pass again between them. "Drink plenty of water," she told her friend. The girl squeezed herself between two others, trying to protect her belly. She held the bag above the girl's head, and two hands appeared from somewhere to grab it from her. The doors shut, only partially, and her friend was gone.

* * * * * * *

Without her charge, something happened to her clarity. Turned around and wandering south, she walked nearly ten blocks in the wrong direction. She stopped repeatedly at pay phones, trying to call home collect. Finally getting through on one, she reached her brother-in-law, the one who had worked at Cantor.

"Thank God," he said relieved, "where are you?" She had one question: their friends, the bride and the groom—did they go to work today, did they go to work today? He was silent a moment. She did not, he replied quietly, but the groom did not have the extra time off—he went to work. She began to sob loudly, uncontrollably. “Stop! Stop it!” he said, “Where are you?” She wasn’t sure; giving an approximation, he instructed her, “I have a friend with an apartment close by: you stay there tonight, tomorrow, too if necessary.” No, she told him, she was going to find a way home, and hung up. She began to walk again, with no real direction.

Then, seeming to appear from nowhere along the sidewalk, she saw a face she recognized, then two more. It was the partners from her firm—the boss and his siblings—walking toward her. They were returning from donating blood for the thousands of injured who would never materialize. The emergency room and makeshift triage outside NYU, standing at the ready, they said, stood eerily empty. The others stared at her for a moment, and exchanged glances at her appearance. She had not said anything.

Sweat stained the blue silk under the armholes of the tank dress.

Her face and shoulders were sun burnt. Her eyes darted nervously about, and she moved constantly. The suit dress was dirty, and struggled to contain her breasts, which had not nursed her baby for hours. She glanced back at them, then reflexively untied the jacket from around her waist and put it on, attempting to close the buttons.

Her boss peered into her face, “Are you okay?” he asked her. He looked around; she was alone. “Where are you going?”

Stammering, she answered, “I’m going . . . I’m . . . I’m not sure.” She stopped for a moment to think, but there was nothing to grasp, none of it made sense anymore. “Home, I think.” Her brow furrowed in thought, “To New Jersey,” she replied finally.

The trio looked at each doubtfully. “The GW, I thought . . . was this way—but . . .” she hesitated, again, “I got as far as 93rd, but . . .” her voice trailed off. The siblings again exchanged glances with each other. “I think I am a little confused,” she stated flatly. “I just need to get home.”

They nodded in agreement and took charge of her.

Ferryboats were still running to New Jersey, they said. She walked with them in silence to the one partner’s apartment, which was nearby. She sat quietly and listened as they discussed what was known: of the Pentagon, the missing planes, the names of the suspected terrorists—whereabouts of friends and loved ones. There they discussed plans, and how she could get home. Her reasonable friend, from earlier, had called while she was there, thankful she was alive—not hurt. He told her to stay with his wife and him—they had a room ready. It made sense, she didn’t feel well.

Her head throbbed; why didn’t anyone understand?

She made a promise in an instant. She was going to do what thousands of people would never be able to do again: she was going home to see her children.

Finally, they determined that the boat was picking up people to go to Monmouth County from the slip at East 35th Street. Her boss had the doorman call a cab, walked her to the curb, wished her luck—and said goodbye with a hug.

The cab sped quickly back downtown on the empty FDR, the late afternoon sun slanting through the window.

She thought back to the discussion at the apartment. First it had focused on the rescue effort. Then, the talk had become angry and animated from the one brother—there would be retaliation, war. And, of course, he had said, the Towers would be rebuilt.

She had been sitting silently, numb. He asked her what she thought.

No, she had said in a dull voice, I don't think it should be rebuilt. She blinked at the colors flashing by the taxi. Thousands are dead . . . the World Trade Center is a graveyard . . . it could only become a memorial. Her head pounded, and she let it rest against the window of the cab.

The ferryboat was loading as she got to the dock. Walking mechanically up the ramp, she heard someone bellowing her childhood nickname, again and again. Then she saw him. The boat captain, an old friend from Bayonne, was shouting and waving to her. His face, mustache, clothes—were filthy. A bandana was tied around his head. He told her he and his crew were among the many boats that had been making runs all day, picking up survivors and the stranded.

From all over downtown, the ferryboats bought people across

the Hudson, some depositing them in Hoboken, others in the Highlands of Jersey. When the day had dragged on without her return, he said he had been asked to keep an eye out for her.

When the ferry docked in New Jersey, there were FBI agents standing on the beach, others in haz-mat suits, with various types of equipment, hoses, and makeshift stalls. An agent called out, "Any person disembarking who was downtown, please step toward the showers, or to the agents with hoses."

He repeated, "If you were downtown, you need to step this way!" She watched as men in business suits were hosed off, first shoes, then pants, and on, upwards. One man stepped out his clothes and was handed a t-shirt and brightly colored shorts by an agent. Another FBI agent asked for her to step forward toward the gentleman with the hose. "Were you downtown, Miss?" She nodded. "And were you at a vantage point to view the plane crash?" he asked.

“Yes,” she replied quietly. The agent took sharper notice, then waited expectantly for more information. “I watched the second plane . . . fly into the building.”

“Where downtown were you? How close?” he asked.

She hesitated at her own words, which would now give validity to the surreal which had transpired, and would play a horrible reel in her head for years to come. “From the street. By Brooks Brothers.”

He raised his eyebrows at her. “You were an eyewitness to the event?” he asked. She nodded again. “We will need to detain you for a little while, and ask you some questions.”

Turning her gaze to the dock where the beach met road, a crowd of anxious faces huddled together, held back by a police line.

Among them, she saw her younger brother standing behind the barricades. Hands in his pockets, he stood silently, watching with the other families, waiting to see if their loved ones would disembark.

The agent looked around at his feet, then said, “I’m sorry, but I don’t think we have any more clothes for you to change into.” The agent softened his tone. “You realize you are carrying dangerous particulate matter on your person.” Her gaze was confused—the man wasn’t making sense. The agent tried again and motioned toward a man being hosed down. “Whatever was down there . . . you don’t want to bring that home—to your family. No, she thought numbly, I don’t want that. “You’ll need to be rinsed off. Okay?”

She nodded again and watched as the hose turned the filthy, blue silk into a dark and unrecognizable color. The agent handed her a towel, and she answered his questions. As the agent spoke and took notes, she answered quietly, succinctly—accurately.

Her brother drove her to their sister's house along the ocean, where her husband, children and other family members had gathered to wait. Crossing the threshold, her sister hugged her tightly, but stopped her from going forward. Smiling, she said quietly "Before you take a shower . . ." she motioned toward her husband across the room, "he has been holding the baby for more than six hours." She looked over at her husband. He did not move toward her. He simply stared at her from where he was.

Her sister held her arm, stopping her again from moving forward. "The baby's been asleep for a very long time—he won't give her to anyone." She spoke in a low voice, " . . . and she hasn't been fed or changed. Can you, please—take her from him?" She nodded numbly.

She walked toward her husband, who was holding the tiny sleeping infant tightly in the crook of one arm. They stared at each other; there was nothing to say. As she put out her hands, he handed her their child, who—at the release—took a huge, deep breath in her sleep. She passed the infant quickly to her sister, but not before touching the indentation left on the child's still soft skull by the grip of her husband's worry.

* * * * * * *

The blue suit was removed, rolled into a plastic grocery bag, and placed out by the trash. Her husband saw it, retrieved it and—without her knowing—placed it into the trunk of her car. The following week, she drove to pick up the baby from her parents' home. Opening the trunk in a shopping plaza parking lot, she was met by a wet, smoky-sick electrical smell. It was the same sorrowful smell that would follow her home from work everyday for nearly a year.

As if struck, she swiped at the bag in defense, then finally grabbed it, head beginning to throb. Walking quickly across the parking lot, heart and head pounding, she stuffed the suit into a trash bin.

Jaws clenching and unclenching in an involuntarily motion, she walked back to her car, heart pounding and nauseous. Out of breath, she quickly jumped into the driver's seat and slammed the car door. She glanced about to see if anyone had seen what she had done. There was no one watching.

As she turned the key in the ignition, her eyes caught sight of the trash barrel. A small, worried piece of blue material hung from the top, stuck in the trap door. It moved slightly in the breeze.

Her teeth ground together. The blood pounding in her ears had become deafening. In nervous confusion, she jumped back out of the car, retrieved the bag, and scanned the stores at the strip mall. Her eyes settled on a dry cleaner's storefront, with a sign that read "Tailoring".

The store bell tinkled as she walked in, and a small, white-haired gentleman greeted her with a smile from behind the counter.

Without friendliness, or a return of his greeting, she dropped the smelly grocery bag onto the counter. He didn't appear rebuffed, and picked up the bag.

"Uh, oh," the tailor started as he opened the bag, "what is this?" His eyebrows knit, then worked up and down, and he clucked at her. "I can't clean this!"

"That's fine," she said reaching to gather it back, keeping her gaze averted, "I was actually going to throw it away." The man moved away, with the suit in his hands.

"Throw it away? No—you can't throw it away!" His voice was too loud, "This is an expensive suit!" He paused for a response; there was none. "But oh, boy—what happened?" He turned the fabric over, ran it through his hands, making small noises. The tailor studied the suit, stopping here and there to examine the damage. "There are stains everywhere . . ." he clucked, and shook his head.

“Really,” she said, “don’t go through any trouble, I probably won’t keep it . . .”

“What is this all over?” he exclaimed. “Water? Some blood? Dirt?” He turned it over and over. “I can’t promise anything here!” His eyes examined the suit skeptically. “Oh, boy.” He brought it to nose. “Whew! Smoke . . .?” He continued on, shaking his head some more, “What happened, did you have a house fire?”

“No.” she tried to say simply, attempting indifference. But her voice caught.

He finally looked up at the woman who had come into his store. Her cheeks and eyes were hollowed; her expression was pained and still. Tears flowed in a continuous stream down both cheeks. He knew immediately.

"Oh, no, no! You . . . were there . . . on that Tuesday?" He put both hands in the air and then covered his mouth. "Don't cry, don't cry!" She knew he wanted badly to comfort her, but she couldn't stop, didn't want to hear it. "We will fix this. It will be beautiful, you will see." His face was full of kindness, but she could tell he didn't understand. "Don't cry, please!"

After wiping her face, she gave him her mother's phone number, and left, never intending to come back.

* * * * * * *

Now, the daily commute could take six or more hours by train, and she had begun to take the ferry regularly in an attempt to see her young children before they fell asleep. Every day, whether coming in to Pier A, or docking at Pier 11, the ferry would fall silent as the boat approached the smoke cloud from the devastation which loomed ahead. The commuters—exchange traders, office workers and exhausted rescue and construction workers—all left the boat the same way, every day—in silence, their footfalls loud on the ramp leading to the pier.

Every day they walked quietly through the rank, stinking air, thick with smoke and ash from the pyre. Some days, tools hanging from the belts of the metal workers knocked together and rang—softly, like chimes, making the only sound in the dark. They walked, on to their work, past weeks of uncollected trash and rotting restaurant food, being feasted upon by rats too bold to run.

Inside Ground Zero, only tenants were allowed access to the darkened buildings. Feared unstable, or designated as part of the crime scene, she crossed . She and other employees walked up flights of stairs to retrieve what they could. They spent weeks, cleaning what they could, gathering files and furniture.

Ultimately, she and her colleagues had to move the office to a new location further down the street. For weeks, she wiped pulverized remains of the Trade Center—all that had passed—from their desks, and terminals and boxes of trade tickets. At first she and the others wore the dust masks on their faces. Then, as they became clogged with suffocating ash, she wore the mask atop her heads.

As soon as one area was wiped cleaned, the dark dust would return to coat the same surface. For weeks, they carried boxes and wheeled office chairs, and file cabinets on carpeted dollies, down the center of Broadway. They learned the catacombs of buildings, and freight elevators, and of secret doors leading from dirty loading bays to polished lobbies. They pushed and carried computers between armed National Guardsmen, past exhausted, gray-faced first responders and piles of rubble, discreetly bulldozed into alleys—like laundry in a closet, stuffed aside to make all appear well.

From the window of the new office, she had a view of the top level of the Battery Park parking garage. The same ash-covered cars remained parked on the roof, in plain sight. They would check the cars silently every day to see if some office worker had been found, miraculously rescued from an air pocket in the rubble, and returned to their family. Months later, they would watch a tow truck—one by one—take them all away.

For months, she walked past the impossibly high "pile"—which would later become "the pit"—watching the emergency workers scramble over twisted metal and rubble in the rescue effort, which would soon become a recovery effort. Some days she left a coffee and sandwich next to a sleeping firefighter or policeman, walking away silently so as not to disturb.

She would go to the gates at St. Paul's Chapel and study the photos of the missing. If someone, her friend, a colleague, a stranger, was wandering downtown, lost and amnesiac, she wanted to know their faces . . . but the photos, there were so many photos. A beautiful young bride, a father hugging a toddler, two handsome men laughing, a graduate, another mom—all loved, at their happiest moments. She repeated their names, and tried to commit their faces to memory, just in case.

She checked the Bloomberg, to look for traders, colleagues, friends, their profile names still active, still alive.

Still alive. Maybe they were not gone. Maybe they were still here, waiting to be found, waiting to go home.

And she found that they were still there. Their sadness clung desperately to the living every day—it left dark blood rings in their nostrils and swelled their eyes. It made their throats bleed, and their lungs heave and cough.

Every day, the workers breathed in the bravery and the fear and the love that hung in the air . . .

. . . and every day, from the smoldering ruin, they carried the ashes of the dead with them, away from that place.

* * * * * * *

"Hello?" she heard her husband answer the phone from their kitchen as she entered the house. A science program went unwatched in another room. "Hey! How are you?" she heard him say to the voice on the phone. "Yeah, I guess it has been awhile."

She had arrived late from work again, and the children had already been bathed and put to bed. After surveying the tangled scatter of toys in the family room, she sighed, and began to tidy up, listening to her husband, comforted by the normal conversation. Several minutes passed until she heard his tone change.

"Oh, well . . . she's doing ok, I guess," he said. "Thanks for asking." She stood silently in the next room and stiffened, her jaws clenched as she began grinding her teeth involuntarily. "Nightmares, yeah . . . jumps at the slightest noise . . ." Her heart was pounding, and she felt her jaw pop. "She had to get on a plane, too. Yeah, end of October . . . that was a rough one." Panic was beginning to flutter in her chest, and she tried a quick breath to quiet it.

"Hmm, yeah, . . . coughing, bloody noses a lot. But they say the air quality down there is OK, so, you know . . . I hope it is." He paused again. "No, nope. She won't talk about that."

The swelling feeling in her chest had moved to her throat, and threatened to choke her. Bile rose, and her teeth clacked and ground. She listened as her husband continued to speak, trapped and suffocating in an open room.

"Well, I don't know, but every day, she comes home smelling bad, like smoke," he said. His voice was low as he continued,

"Yeah, like a campfire, but . . . not the same." A pause. "Yeah, like that. She always asks if I can smell it . . . I just tell her no."

The room swam and spun. Translucent lenses of tears clogged her vision. The toys at her feet became a kaleidoscope—every form touching the next, bleeding into one another, indiscernible from the whole.

* * * * * * *

Weeks later, her mother left a message on the answering machine: "Honey, I wanted to check with you. Um, . . . a dry cleaner nearby keeps calling, said we left something there? I don't use them . . . Did you? I wasn't sure." A pause. "I love you. Call me."

Ashamed with herself, she drove south to the dry cleaners the next day.

The store bell tinkled once, then again with the gust of cold air at her back as she entered. This time, no one was behind the counter. Rather than ring the call bell on the counter, she stood in the dusty sunlight of the storefront, waiting quietly, enveloped in the warmth of the late morning sun and the clean, safe smell of laundered clothes. Finally, the old man ventured forth and saw her.

"I'm so sorry it's taken me this long . . ." she began to confess.

"Oh!" the dry cleaner clapped his hands together when he saw her, "Oh, I am so happy you came back!" She gave a sad smile at his greeting. "Wait, wait, let me get it for you!" he said and shuffled off. He returned, carrying the blue suit before him. He stopped in front of her and removed the shroud of plastic.

The color was completely different—softened now, aged it seemed, to a somber, cadet blue. He turned it around, showing her where he tailored the rear vent that had split when she fell. Holding it first to his nose, then to hers, he said, "See, no smell."

His forehead creased, and he frowned a bit. "But the stains were so dark . . . they will never come out completely . . ."

His face was full of the effort of a work performed out of sadness, and the need to do something to help. "I had to soak them in, make them part of the fabric." Looking up, he smiled at her. "But, you can't see them unless you hold it to the light." And he demonstrated.

It was true. The suit certainly wasn't new, and it appeared very different . . . but it was beautiful. Her heart ached. "I don't know how to thank you . . ."

He smiled and nodded his head, "I was happy to do it." He reached out and patted her hand. She started to open her purse, and he quickly waved a hand. "You wear it in good health." He smiled at her. "Take care, my dear," he said, then gave her a hug before she left.

Stopping next to her car, she held the suit up. A small piece of index card, cut by hand, was safety-pinned to the plastic. In perfect, shaky script it read: *girl from WTC*.

Once again, she pulled off the plastic wrap. She began to examine the suit, closely now, one more time.

The sun shone down out of a brilliant blue sky, but the breeze now was cold. She shivered, and reached out to touch the dress. She was surprised at how sturdy—but soft—the material felt under her fingers. It had become completely changed. And although the texture seemed rougher, raised—no one piece, no thread, could appear to be separated from the others. The now familiar lump filled her chest, and rose to her throat.

Holding the suit up to the sun, they appeared: small, shadowy shapes, that seemed to move about in the soft, glowing, blue fabric.

EPILOGUE

Tuesday, March 8, 2016

Throughout the construction years, when she commuted to work, she usually took the ferryboat to Pier 11. At first, the downtown commuters crammed onto too few ferries, the only reasonable way to get to the financial district. Through the cold winter of 2001, men and women, most in suits, some in construction gear, huddled together against the wind off the Atlantic Ocean. Stoically, they chugged from the smoldering ruins, briefcases in hand on the outside decks, beneath greasy black plumes of diesel smoke.

Although she had taken the PATH train to World Trade occasionally, she tended to avoid it.

Now, it had been some time since she commuted regularly. She was unaware of the Oculus, its construction, the intent of its architecture or any controversy over design. She was unaware the new space had just opened to the public two or three days earlier.

Her meeting near Bowling Green had run long. Approaching Trinity Church, she knew she would not make it down the length of Wall Street to catch the next boat.
Reluctantly, she decided to take the PATH train instead, and crossed Broadway to cut through the church graveyard.

Starting toward the place where the Trade Center had stood, she found it unrecognizable. She had never been to the Memorial before, and walked uneasily past tourists taking photos. Relieved at seeing doors with escalators just beyond, she entered and descended below.

But the path continued on, through an all-white maze of walk-ways, newly lit by a fluorescent glow. Here and there, construction crews worked, oblivious of the passersby, the whine of electric machinery assaulting her ears.

Confused, she walked on until, from somewhere ahead, she saw natural light. At first stepping toward it, she stopped abruptly. It was an large openness, all white.

Standing frozen, she looked across the cavernous space, which was flooded with light. Only several people were there, off to the sides of the great clearing. No one spoke, because even the smallest whisper was amplified and startling.

Her mind scanned and reviewed the space, looking for something familiar. There was only one. Across the distance, away from the light, escalators with gleaming turnstiles before them, led down to the New Jersey trains.

Looking for the many places that went before, her mind worked: no busy underground mall, no open metal framework and concrete platforms, no exposed walls of giant rebar, no particleboard walkways and plastic sheeting.

Now there was only light. And long, white, delicate bones—rising high above—to meet the bright afternoon sun.

She walked close to the walls, then slowly stepped into the empty, open space.

For the first time, she felt something she had not felt in that place, after that time: quiet. It was not peace.

It was merely silence. Simple. Elegant. Silence.

Lowering herself to sit on the broad, curved stair, she stayed to listen for it.

She did not see the Port Authority police officer until he was standing beside her. She looked up from where she sat and smiled up at him.

Without saying a word, he smiled back at her. Then, after a moment, he spoke:

"You know . . ." his voice was deep and kind, but he hesitated. Then, with a bit of reluctance, he continued. "You know," he said, clearing his throat, "you can't stay here."

She looked back across the open space. The enormous flag, the long bones, the afternoon light.

"I know," she said.

But, she thought, if I can linger here a bit longer . . .

She turned to look up at him again. “Thank you,” she replied.

He smiled at her, then walked back to his post by the turnstile.

She ran one hand across the smooth, white floor. Then she got up from the empty place, and went home.

—The Oculus

About the Author

Michaela DiBernardo Ferrigine is a freelance writer and investment professional in New York. Born and raised in Hudson County, she began writing in high school after her family moved to the Jersey Shore. An artist and writer at heart, Michaela entered the field of institutional finance shortly after college.

A week after returning from maternity leave to the NYSE firm where she worked, Michaela became an eyewitness to, and survivor of 9/11. The tragedy completely altered her perception of life and became a part of her every day. A member of The World Trade Center Health Registry from 2004, she eventually realized that generations of young people may not understand the tremendous loss and palpable grief of that time. Michaela decided to publish the narrative nonfiction work, "The Blue Suit: A 9/11 Memoir" in the third person, to record her personal history.

The suit she wore that tragic day—nearly discarded as a painful reminder—moved from a place of honor in the back of her closet to the permanent collection at the National September 11 Memorial & Museum in New York.

In addition to nonfiction work, Michaela writes short stories and poetry. She earned her B.A. from Rutgers University, and currently resides at the Jersey Shore with her husband, family, and many rescue pets.

Made in USA - Kendallville, IN
31338_9780578695822
10.08.2022 1301